CW00956500

CLASSIC

THUNDERBIRDS

The Little Book of

THUNDERBIRD 2

THIS IS A CARLTON BOOK

Published by Carlton Books Limited 2003
20 Mortimer Street
London W1T 3JW

Text and design copyright © 2003 Carlton Publishing Group

™ and © 1964, 1999 and 2003 ITC Entertainment Group Ltd.
THUNDERBIRDS is a Gerry Anderson Production.
Licensed by Carlton International Media Limited.
www.thunderbirdsonline.com

A CIP catalogue record for this book is available from the
British Library.

ISBN 1 84442 898 2

The Little Book of

THUNDERBIRD 2

INTERNATIONAL RESCUE'S HEAVY-DUTY EQUIPMENT TRANSPORTER

CARLTON
BOOKS

CONTENTS

THUNDERBIRD 2

FACT FILE

Thunderbird 2 is International Rescue's heavy-duty freighter which carries the organization's auxiliary rescue equipment to the danger zone.

It is housed in a hangar beneath the Cliff House, which overlooks the runway on Tracy island. The ship is 250 feet long, with a wing span of 80 feet and it stands 60 feet high.

Pilot Virgil Tracy gains access to his vehicle via a tilting picture in the lounge of the villa. This tips him on to a padded slide which glides down a chute.

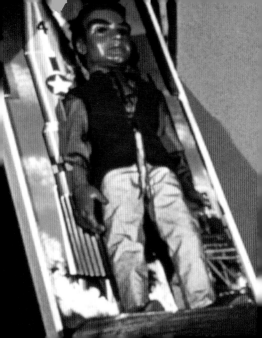

The chute levels out and the slide comes to a stop on a turntable which revolves so that Virgil is facing feet first as he continues his journey down the chute and directly into his seat in the cockpit of Thunderbird 2.

The central section of the craft carries one of a selection of six interchangeable pods, each housing different auxiliary vehicles. Virgil selects the appropriate pod as it passes on a conveyor belt beneath and hydraulic legs drop the main fuselage into place over the pod.

THUNDERBIRD 2

A steel door disguised as a section of the cliff wall then moves down into a trench at the hangar end of the runway and a second 'drawbridge door' swings down to cover the trench and provide smooth access to the runway.

As an airstrip that would accommodate the full width of Thunderbird 2's wing span would draw attention to itself, the

runway is lined with movable palm trees which fall back to allow Thunderbird 2 passage to a concealed launch ramp.

On arrival at the danger zone, Thunderbird 2 lands and then lifts clear of the pod on its hydraulic legs to enable unloading operations. Pod 4 is fitted with flotation equipment which enables it to be released over water.

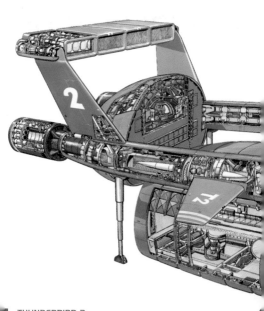

THUNDERBIRD 2

THUNDERBIRD 2

CROSS-SECTIONS

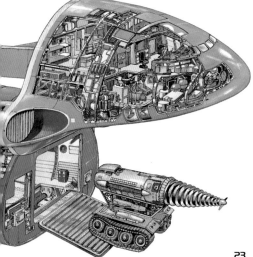

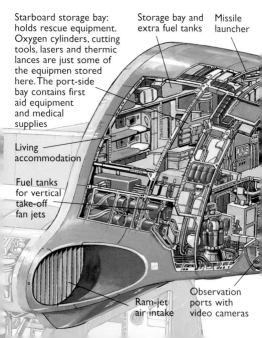

Starboard storage bay: holds rescue equipment. Oxygen cylinders, cutting tools, lasers and thermic lances are just some of the equipmen stored here. The port-side bay contains first aid equipment and medical supplies

Storage bay and extra fuel tanks

Missile launcher

Living accommodation

Fuel tanks for vertical take-off fan jets

Ram-jet air intake

Observation ports with video cameras

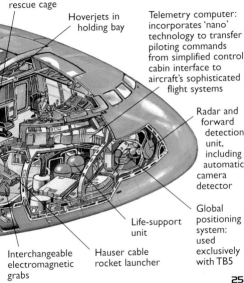

Passenger lift: allows extra crew members access to pilot's cabin seating. Lift also descends to allow access rescue cage

Hoverjets in holding bay

Telemetry computer: incorporates 'nano' technology to transfer piloting commands from simplified control cabin interface to aircraft's sophisticated flight systems

Radar and forward detection unit, including automatic camera detector

Life-support unit

Global positioning system: used exclusively with TB5

Interchangeable electromagnetic grabs

Hauser cable rocket launcher

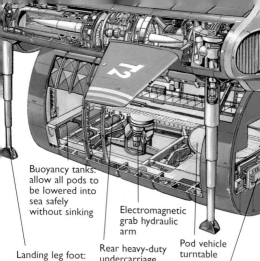

Buoyancy tanks: allow all pods to be lowered into sea safely without sinking

Electromagnetic grab hydraulic arm

Pod vehicle turntable

Landing leg foot: contains vertical-thrust rocket to aid take-off and landing

Rear heavy-duty undercarriage rollers

One of four forward electromagnetic docking clamps that hold the pod in place during flight

THUNDERBIRD 2

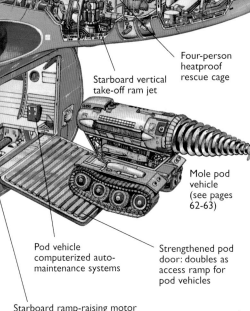

Four-person heatproof rescue cage

Starboard vertical take-off ram jet

Mole pod vehicle (see pages 62-63)

Pod vehicle computerized auto-maintenance systems

Strengthened pod door: doubles as access ramp for pod vehicles

Starboard ramp-raising motor

27

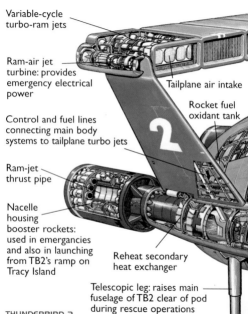

Variable-cycle
turbo-ram jets

Ram-air jet
turbine: provides
emergency electrical
power

Tailplane air intake

Rocket fuel
oxidant tank

Control and fuel lines
connecting main body
systems to tailplane turbo jets

Ram-jet
thrust pipe

Nacelle
housing
booster rockets:
used in emergencies
and also in launching
from TB2's ramp on
Tracy Island

Reheat secondary
heat exchanger

Telescopic leg: raises main
fuselage of TB2 clear of pod
during rescue operations

THUNDERBIRD 2

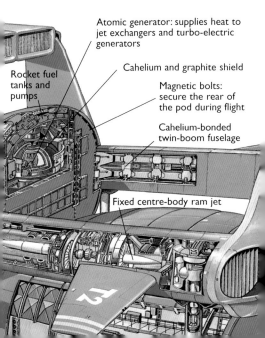

Atomic generator: supplies heat to jet exchangers and turbo-electric generators

Cahelium and graphite shield

Rocket fuel tanks and pumps

Magnetic bolts: secure the rear of the pod during flight

Cahelium-bonded twin-boom fuselage

Fixed centre-body ram jet

TM

CLASSIC THUNDERBIRDS

MARTIAN INVASION

Virgil Defeats the Hood!

Sally Byford

The Hood had a plan to uncover International Rescue's secrets. He travelled to the desert in disguise to work on a film called Martian Invasion.

In the film the Martians had to bomb a cave where two police officers were hiding. The Hood planned to cause a terrible accident so that International Rescue would have to be called out.

Then he'd film them in action and sell their secrets to the mysterious General X.

First, the Hood needed help from his half-brother, Kyrano, who worked for International Rescue. In his temple, he used magic to get Kyrano in his power.

"Go to Thunderbird I," the Hood ordered Kyrano, "and switch off the automatic camera detector."

So, while Kyrano was under the Hood's spell, he crept over to Thunderbird I and switched off the detector. Now the Hood would be able to film the aircraft without Scott knowing.

When the filming started, the two actors playing police officers hid in a cave and the Martians bombed them. Everyone was shocked by the size of the explosion. They did not know that the Hood had been at work. The cave started to collapse and water poured in.

"We'd better call International Rescue," said the Hood.

Mr Goldheimer, the director, called for help. "Two of the actors are trapped," he told Jeff Tracy. "Please come quickly!"

Scott and Virgil soon arrived in Thunderbirds 1 and 2. As soon as they saw what had happened, Virgil released the Excavator and started drilling through the rocks that blocked the cave's entrance.

Meanwhile the Hood was secretly filming every detail of International Rescue's equipment.

"My plan is working perfectly."

Inside the cave, the two actors playing the police officers were very scared. They clung to the rocks, but the water was rising fast. Suddenly they heard Scott's voice on the radio.

"Stay calm," he said. "When I give the word, jump into the water. The pressure will carry you out through the hole we have drilled in the side of the mountain. Now, jump!"

The men jumped. They knew it was their only chance.

POLICE

The two actors shot out of the hole just before the cave roof collapsed. They were wet and shivering, but they were safe. The rescue had been a success.

Scott was about to leave in Thunderbird 1 when Mr Goldheimer rushed up and took a photograph of him.

The camera detector didn't sound its alarm. Scott was puzzled.

"It must be switched off," he said. "Someone could have taken a film of the whole rescue."

Suddenly, they heard a Jeep speeding away.
Mr Goldheimer looked through his binoculars.
It was the Hood, without his disguise.

"That man's stolen a reel of film," he cried.

Scott knew it could be a film of the rescue.
He chased after the Hood in Thunderbird 1,
but the Jeep vanished into a tunnel.

The Hood called General X.

"I'll deliver the film as
soon as I have escaped
from International
Rescue," he said.

Scott stopped outside the tunnel and contacted his father.

"There are two entrances to that tunnel, Scott," said Jeff. "I'll send Virgil in Thunderbird 2 to take your place. You must go to the other entrance."

"I'm on my way, father," said Scott.

"Don't let that film get away," said Jeff. "If our secrets are discovered, it will be the end of International Rescue."

As soon as Scott had left to find the other entrance, the Hood made his escape. Virgil arrived just in time to see him driving away at top speed. Quickly, he contacted his father.

"Do everything you can to stop him, Virgil," said Jeff. "We've got to get that film."

Virgil bombed the mountains at the side of the road. There was a landslide and the Hood's Jeep was trapped.

The Hood jumped out of his Jeep and ran off. He hadn't gone far when he saw an empty plane. "Perfect!" he said, and he climbed in and took off.

He called General X on his radio to tell him that he had managed to escape from International Rescue and would soon be handing over the film. But then he realized that there was something wrong with the plane. It was dropping towards the ground because the controls were not working properly.

Scott was following close behind.

At last the Hood saw General X's villa ahead, but by now he couldn't control the plane at all. Scott watched as it crashed into the front of the villa. This was the end of the Hood's evil plan.

Scott contacted his father. "The film couldn't have survived that smash," he said.

"Well done," said Jeff. "Thanks to you and Virgil the Hood has been beaten and International Rescue's secrets are safe. This mission is now complete."

VIRGIL TRACY

The most serious of the Tracy brothers, Virgil was born on 15 August 2041 and is now twenty-four years old. He was named after 20th Century astronaut Virgil Grissom.

Virgil is an accomplished graduate of the Denver School of Advanced Technology. This gives him the experience and mechanical dexterity he needs to pilot Thunderbird 2 and its various auxiliary rescue vehicles.

Like his brothers, Virgil never places technology above human needs, even if it means placing his own life in danger. He is always on hand, taking part in virtually every daring situation in which International Rescue is involved.

Possessing a demeanour and maturity well beyond his years, Virgil is a complex young man who combines a physical strength and fearless bravery with a gentler side as a gifted artist and pianist.

DESIGNED FOR DANGER

The Mole

The Mole is one of the larger pod vehicles, weighing 30 tons. It is used to help recover victims trapped in collapsed buildings or buried underground. Despite its size and tremendous power, the Mole can be operated with great precision so that buried victims are not endangered by rock falls started by the movement of the drill.

THUNDERBIRD 2

The Domo

The Demolition and Object Moving Operator uses artificial-gravity fields within its three suction pods to stabilize walls or lift objects weighing up to 50 tons. It is used to clear the disaster zone of heavy objects or secure dangerous buildings prior to the use of other vehicles such as the Mole.

Elevator Cars

Built for use at airports, the high-speed Elevator Cars can match the speed of most incoming aircraft unable to use their undercarriage for landing safely.

The Firefly

Combining fire-fighting, site-clearance and demolition roles, the Firefly is one of International Rescue's main pod vehicles. It has a cahelium extract X-built shield that performs a dual role as dozer blade and high-impact protective blast shield.

Transmitter Truck

Adapted from a heavy-duty commercial vehicle, the truck uses a Jodrell Six multi-use dish for transmitting radio safety and tractor beams, plus computer data and communications signals to or from inaccessible areas.

Recovery Vehicles

These are used to drag heavy metal objects out of danger, Recovery Vehicles have magnetic clamps that can be fired up to 300 feet and powerful winches that then haul the objects in.

The Mobile Crane

This is a six-wheeled truck equipped with a telescopic arm that can raise a maintenance platform up to heights of around 50 feet.

Fire Truck

Another formerly commercial vehicle
adapted for use by International
Rescue, the Fire Truck has been
modified to fight any kind of fire.
As well as having powerful water
pumps and foam-storage tanks, it
can also snuff out fires or create
firebreaks by the use of nitro-
glycerine shells.

TECHNICAL DATA

LENGTH: .... 250 feet

WINGSPAN: .... 180 feet

DIAMETER: .... 60 feet

EXTENDED HEIGHT WITH POD LOWERED:
.... 110 feet

WEIGHT: .... 406 tons [ex.payload]

PAYLOAD: .... up to 100 tons

MAXIMUM SPEED: .. 5,000m.p.h

CRUISING SPEED: .. 2,000m.p.h

MAXIMUM ALTITUDE ATTAINED: 100,000 feet

RANGE: .... unlimited

POWER SOURCE: .... atomic fusion reactor

ENGINES:

   2 variable-cycle gas turbine engines
     operating as turbo fans at low speed
     and supersonic combustion ram jets at
     high speed

   12 variable-cycle turbo-ram cruise/trim jets
      in tailplane

   4 vertical take-off turbo fan jets in main body

   4 vertical take-off chemical rockets in
     landing legs

PILOT: .... Virgil Tracy

75

Launch Ramp

When Thunderbird 2 is ready to launch, the palm trees lining the runway fall away and a section of the runway itself is raised by hydraulics to an angle of 45 degrees.

Thunderbird 2 Hangar

Located behind a hidden door cut into the rock under the Cliff House is the enormous hangar that houses Thunderbird 2 and its six detachable pods. It also contains a workshop area and specialist rescue equipment.

Thunderbird 5

Thunderbird 2

THUNDERBIRD 2

PUT IN PERSPECTIVE

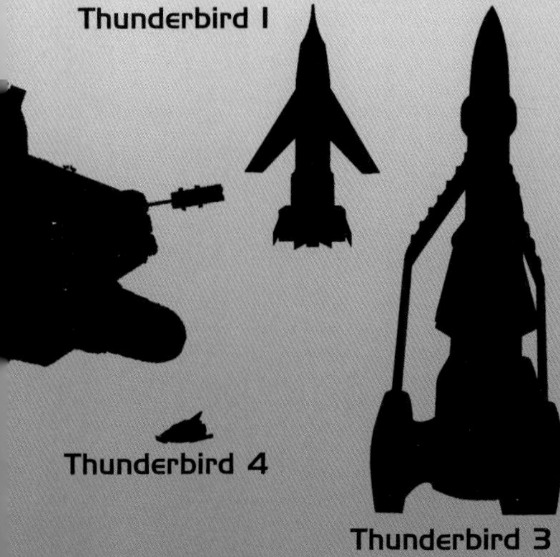

Thunderbird 1

Thunderbird 4

Thunderbird 3